KT-366-964

Violin
Scales &
Arpeggios

Why practise scales?

Welcome to this book of scales and arpeggios for
Grade 4 Violin. Practising scales and arpeggios plays an
essential part in developing a violinist's skills, and time
devoted to these exercises within each practice session
will improve every aspect of playing. Not only can
many areas of violin technique be developed through
scale practice, but the sense of key and pattern acquired
through familiarity with scales and arpeggios has
several benefits: it speeds up the learning of new pieces,
develops fine intonation and evenness of line and tone,
builds aural awareness, and increases familiarity with
the geography of the violin.

For the exam

Tempo

The candidate should aim for a tempo that achieves
a clean, sonorous tone, vitality of rhythm, controlled
bowing, and good intonation.

Bowing

Slurred scales and arpeggios should be played with
the whole bow wherever possible and this bowing
will inevitably affect the tempo. Scales and arpeggios
using separate bows should be played briskly and
with a smooth *détaché*, using no more than half the
bow length.

Fingering

Fingering is suggested from Grade 3 upwards. From
Grade 4, two fingering patterns are sometimes offered,
one in standard print above the stave and the other in
italic below. All given fingering is thought to be practical
and consistent – but is not compulsory. There are many
different ways of fingering scales and arpeggios,
bearing in mind ease of performance, memorability,
and the importance of changing position unobtrusively,
and candidates should experiment to find solutions that
work for them. (Examiners will not comment on the
choice of fingering, unless it interferes with the
performance.) Note that, when in the first position,
either an open string or the fourth finger may be used.

On the day

All scales and arpeggios must be played from memory.
The examiner will ask for at least one of each type of
scale or arpeggio required at the grade, and will aim to
hear a balance of both slurred and separate bows.

The examiner will be looking for:

- good intonation across the pitch range
- an even and positive sense of rhythm
- accurate and fluent realization of the different
  types of scales and arpeggios
- confident, controlled, and consistent tone
- convincing negotiation of technical challenges
  such as string crossing, position changing, and
  bow co-ordination.

Reference must always be made to the syllabus for the year in
which the exam is to be taken, in case any changes have been
made to the requirements.

General information on the exam can be found in *Examination
Information and Regulations*, and in the guide for candidates,
teachers and parents *These Music Exams*. These and the syllabus
document are available online at www.abrsm.org, as well as free
of charge from music retailers, from ABRSM local representatives
or from the Services Department, The Associated Board of the
Royal Schools of Music, 24 Portland Place, London W1B 1LU,
United Kingdom.

© 2007 by The Associated Board of the Royal Schools of Music

SCALES

two octaves

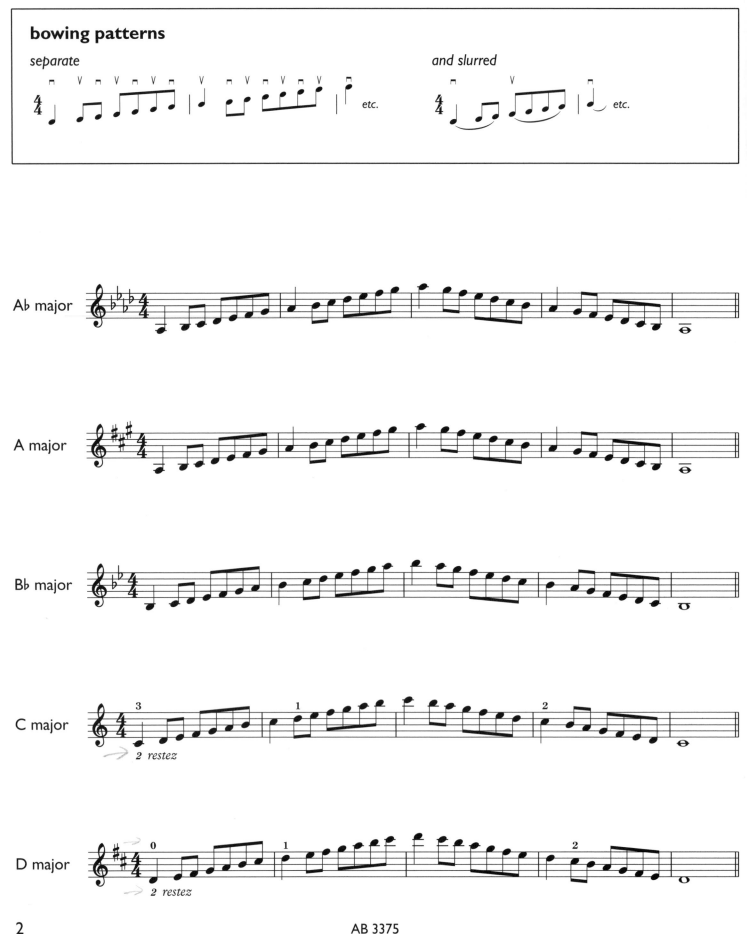

ARPEGGIOS

two octaves

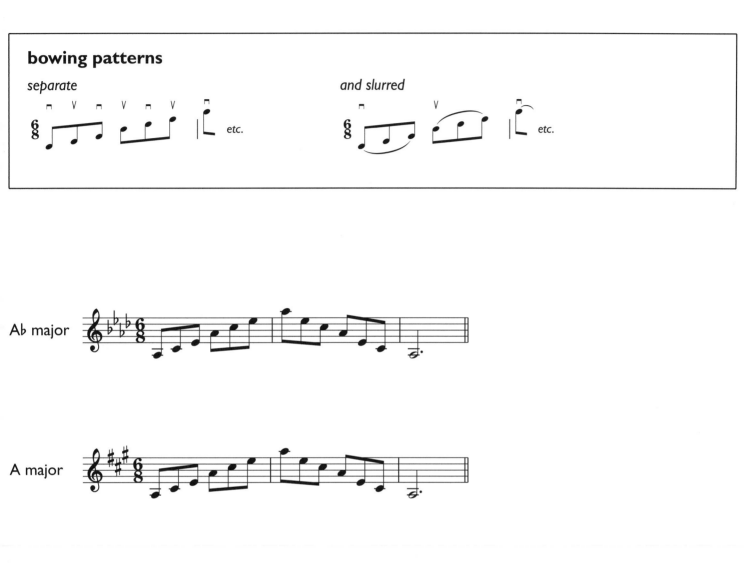

Ab major

A major

Bb major

C major

D major

SCALES (cont.)

two octaves (cont.)

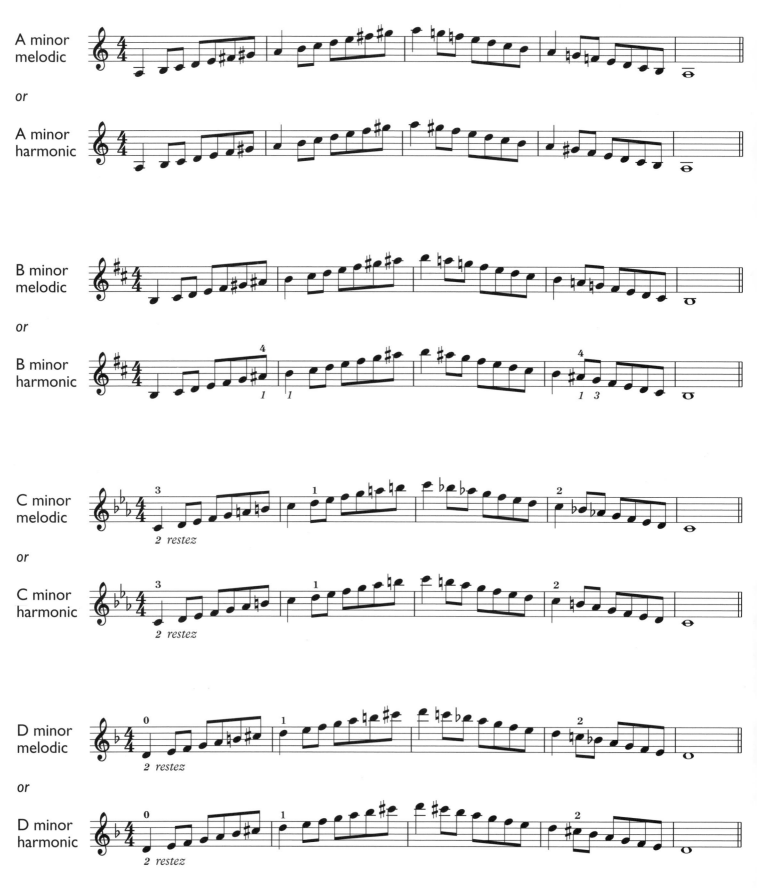

A minor
melodic

or

A minor
harmonic

B minor
melodic

or

B minor
harmonic

C minor
melodic

or

C minor
harmonic

D minor
melodic

or

D minor
harmonic

ARPEGGIOS (cont.)

two octaves (cont.)

A minor

B minor

C minor

D minor

CHROMATIC SCALES

one octave

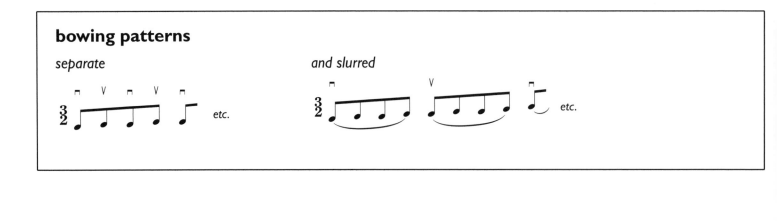

AB 3375

DOMINANT SEVENTHS

one octave

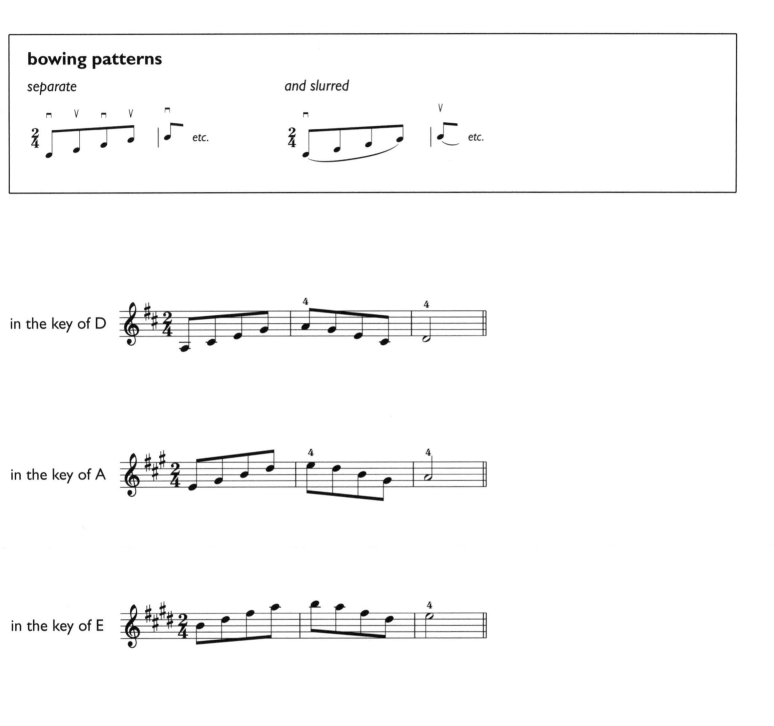

Printed in England by Halstan & Co. Ltd, Amersham, Bucks